This book belongs to:

Charlotte

hap·py

-feeling or showing pleasure or contentment.

-fortunate and convenient.

Bee-ing Happy
With Unicorn Jazz
and Friends

By
Lisa Caprelli

Illustrator
Davey Villalobos

Bee-ing Happy With Unicorn Jazz and Friends

Part of the Unicorn Jazz TM Series by Lisa Caprelli

Illustrated by Davey Villalobos

Published by Happy & Fun Lifestyle LLC

Library of Congress Control Number: 2019909736

Copyright 2019

All rights reserved

ISBN: 978-1-951203-00-9

Dedicated to my love for finding joy in the five hats: family, friendship, career, connection and adventure! —Lisa

Dear friend,

My name is Bee Happy! I am proud to be friends with Unicorn Jazz and animals you will find throughout this book and my next book in the Unicorn Jazz series.

I SEE YOU!

You will find me, the bee, hidden in some pages in this book. Have fun finding me.

We had a blast with the author and illustrator to create different ideas for happiness. I am sure you have many of your own, too!

Enjoy exploring and don't forget to look at the Bee-ing Happy discussion questions at the end of this book along with some fun facts. If you are interested, send us photos of you reading the book or other happy moments for Instagram or Facebook.

Bee Happy!

Sincerely,

Lisa Caprelli

UnicornJazz.com

Bee-ing Happy Is...

Making up silly words.

Bee-ing Happy Is...

Writing a thoughtful letter.

Bee-ing Happy Is...

Painting something new.

Bee-ing Happy Is...

Giving someone a balloon.

Bee-ing Happy Is...

Walking on the beach.

Bee-ing Happy Is...

♪ Dancing with friends. ♪

Bee-ing Happy Is...

Playing make believe.

Bee-ing Happy Is...

Bringing your teacher flowers.

Bee-ing Happy Is...

Enjoying nature.

Bee-ing Happy Is...

Making s'mores at your campsite.

Bee-ing Happy Is...

Making someone laugh!

Bee-ing Happy Is...

Greeting someone at the door.

Bee-ing Happy Is...

Baking sweets with mom.

Bee-ing Happy Is...

Day or night
later or soon
i love you
to the moon...

I ♥ U
2 THE
🌙

Dad reading to you.

Bee-ing Happy Is...

Helping someone learn.

Bee-ing Happy Is...

Petting your cat.

Bee-ing Happy Is...

Jumping with a friend.

Bee-ing Happy Is...

Trying on mom's favorite dress.

Bee-ing Happy Is...

Watching a beautiful sunset.

Bee-ing Happy Is...

Belonging.

Bee-ing Happy Is...

Catching snowflakes.

Bee-ing Happy Is...

Coloring together!

Check out my Bee-ing Happy Coloring Book with
many animals seen in this book on UnicornJazz.com

10 Questions to Explore Using Your Imagination.

1. What else makes you happy on this page?

2. What do you want to do outside today?

3. Who would be happy if they got a letter from you?

4. What can we do to help make someone happy?

5. What are 3 things that you are grateful for?

6. What could you do for someone else?

7. What does being happy mean to you?

8. What was your favorite part of today?

9. What part of that can we learn more about?

10. When do you feel happiest?

FUN FACTS

Did you know? Quills were the primary writing instrument in the west ern world from the 6th to the 19th century. The best *quills were* usually made from goose, swan, and later turkey feathers.

Quill pens *were* the *instrument* of choice during the medieval era due to their compatibility with parchment and vellum. Quills went into decline after the invention of the metal pen, mass production beginning in Great Britain as early as 1822 by John Mitchell of Birmingham. A quill pen is a writing implement made from a moulted flight feather.

The word *balloon* likely comes from the Italian word 'pallone' meaning 'large ball'. In the 1570s, *balloon* was a popular game played using a large in-flated leather ball that was kicked or tossed back and forth; by the 1590s, the word *balloon* was used to refer to the ball itself. By 1784, *balloon* was also used to describe a 'bag or vessel filled with heated air or helium so as to rise and float in the air'.

FUN FACTS

The modern pogo stick was invented by Max Pohlig and Ernst Gottschall, from Germany. A German patent was registered in Hanover on March 1920 for a device they called a "spring end hopping stilt". It is thought that the beginning two letters in these men's last names is where the word "pogo" comes from.

Belonging. Woof the Crow represents someone who believes in you. In the first Unicorn Jazz book, Woof the Crow, helps Jazz realize her talent, which is singing. Sometimes it takes just one person to believe in you. Who believes in you?

The American patriotic song, America the Beautiful, include the verse: "Purple mountain majesties" which refers to the shade of the Pikes Peak in Colorado Springs, Colorado, inspired by Katharine Lee Bates in 1895 when she wrote the poem. The music was later composed by church organist Samuel Ward in 1910. Ward's music combined with the Bates poem. The song is one of the most popular U.S. patriotic songs.

Source: Wikipedia

SHELLS ON THE BEACH

Is the Ocean Sound inside this shell?
What sounds like ocean wave noise when you hold a shell up to your ear is just the movement of air across and through the shell.

You could hear similar sounds if you were to hold a bowl or a cup up to your ear. Stop and listen!

Is this shell alive?
When you first pick up a shell at the beach, if it is not obvious that the shell is living it is still possible that there is an animal inside the shell. To determine if it is still alive, you will need to observe it for awhile, leave it alone and watch for a few minutes. For example, hermit crabs are commonly hiding inside their shell. Usually the animal will feel safe enough to begin to crawl out of the shell and explore its surroundings. Be sure to release it back where you found it.

When is the best time to collect shells?
A good time to find shells is at low tides.
You can explore what tide means and check tide times on the internet.

About The Author

Lisa Caprelli is a proud Latina mom who grew up with humble beginnings, but found her voice in writing. She is the visionary creator for the Unicorn Jazz stories and brand, along with several other books for adults and young minds of all ages, like "Skip a Step: Imparting Wisdom for Young Entrepreneur Minds." She graduated magna cum laude with a Bachelor's of Science Degree in Social Psychology and her quest for studying human behavior is seen in her author visits, school visits, hospital and community messages with kids, parents and educators. Lisa's ambitious and multi-faceted perspective inspires people all around her to live a life of purpose. Born and raised in El Paso, Texas she now resides in Orange County, California with her family. As a writer, marketer and business development leader with over 25 yrs of experience, having worked with numerous of CEO's, she is called upon for strategy, motivation and inspiration. She enjoys speaking and teaching diverse audiences of all ages: toddlers, elementary schools, teens, educators, parents, counselors, librarians and more.

About The Illustrator

Davey Villalobos resides in El Paso, Texas with his family and siblings. He has been drawing his whole life as early as age 4. Davey does 90% of his work alfresco while listening to music (from the smooth sounds of Dean Martin to the ear blasting riffs of Slayer). Some of his favorite illustrators are Salvador Dali, Frank Frazzetta, Bob Kane (Batman). He enjoys being creative, intuitive and letting his imagination run wild. Davey will be publishing his first book this year. He is a proud uncle of two and enjoys bike riding.

im·ag·i·na·tion

Imagination - the faculty or action of forming new ideas, or images or concepts of external objects not present to the senses.

If you like this book, please review on Amazon or Goodreads.

We thrive on positive reviews and feedback!

Unicorn Jazz™ is a series created by Happy & Fun Lifestyle LLC

UnicornJazz.com

Instagram.com/UnicornJazzBrand

More Books & Products By Unicorn Jazz™

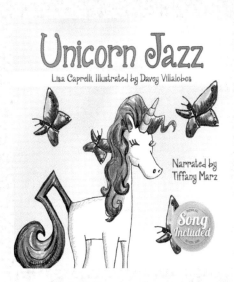

The Unicorn Jazz Friendship song sung By Kerri Kasem with sing-a-long lyrics is on UnicornJazz.com and on YouTube!

Hear the story come to life on audiobook format— Audible!

Instagram.com/UnicornJazzBrand

Made in the USA
Monee, IL
03 February 2020